This Peppa Pig book
belongs to

....

LADYBIRD BOOKS

UK | USA | Canada | Ireland | Australia
India | New Zealand | South Africa

Ladybird Books is part of the Penguin Random House group of companies
whose addresses can be found at global.penguinrandomhouse.com.
www.penguin.co.uk   www.puffin.co.uk   www.ladybird.co.uk

Penguin
Random House
UK

First published 2018
001

This book is based on the TV series *Peppa Pig*.
Peppa Pig is created by Neville Astley and Mark Baker.
Peppa Pig © Astley Baker Davies Ltd/Entertainment One UK Ltd 2003.
www.peppapig.com

Printed in China

A CIP catalogue record for this book is available from the British Library
ISBN: 978-0-241-32154-6

All correspondence to:
Ladybird Books, Penguin Random House Children's,
80 Strand, London, WC2R 0RL

Contents

Changing Seasons

This is Peppa.

This is George.

This is Mummy Pig.

This is Daddy Pig.

Peppa, George and their family love all the different seasons – spring, summer, autumn and winter! Look at their pictures and circle the right answers to the questions.

It's spring. What do you think might hatch from the eggs?

It's summer. What should Mummy Pig wear in the paddling pool?

It's autumn. What colour are some of the fallen leaves?

Which is your favourite season? Draw yourself with Peppa and George in your favourite season.

It's winter. What's the best way to travel in the snow?

Downhill Dash!

Wheeee! Peppa and George are skiing!
Draw a line to help them weave their way in and out of the
trees to the finish. Who will they see at the bottom?

How many snowmen did you count on the way?

Finish

Answers: They will see Santa at the bottom.
There are four snowmen on the way down.

Penguin Spotting

Mummy and Daddy Pig have taken Peppa and George penguin spotting. Wow, look at all those penguins waddling along! Can you circle the odd one out in each line?

Pretend to waddle just like a penguin!

Story Time

When I Grow Up!

It is a lovely sunny playgroup afternoon for Peppa, George and their friends. "Children," begins Madame Gazelle, "today we are going to talk about what you would like to be when you grow up."
"Ooooh!" gasps everyone.

Madame Gazelle tells the children they can use the dressing-up box to help them decide what they want to be.

"When I grow up," says Rebecca Rabbit, putting on a crown, "I want to be a queen so I can tell people what to do!"

"I want to be a teacher," says Emily Elephant. She pretends to be Madame Gazelle.
"Children! Sit down! Come here! Quiet, now! Listen to me!"
"Very good," says Madame Gazelle. "What do you like about being
a teacher, Emily?"
"Telling people what to do!" Emily replies.

"I want to be a policeman when I grow up," says Freddy Fox. "The police solve
mysteries and drive cars with flashing lights! *Nee-naa! Nee-naa! Whoooo!*"
"Thank you, Freddy!" says Madame Gazelle. "What else do you like about
being a policeman?"
"They tell people what to do!" says Freddy.

Next to stand up is Suzy Sheep. "I would like to be a doctor or a nurse," she says.
"Why do you want that job, Suzy?" asks Madame Gazelle.
"Because doctors and nurses help sick people get better," replies Suzy. "And they tell people what to do!"
"Not all jobs are about telling people what to do," says Madame Gazelle.

"When I grow up, I will be a pirate. Yo-ho-ho!" says Danny Dog. "Or a farmer."
"A farmer sounds good," says Madame Gazelle. "You would grow food to eat."
"And I'd get to tell all the animals what to do!" adds Danny.

"I will be a superhero!" says Pedro Pony.

"I see," says Madame Gazelle. "Well, you know being a superhero is a very important job. You have to run faster than a train, jump tall buildings and –"

"Yes, I don't want to do all of those super things," explains Pedro. "But I do want to tell people what to do."

Now it's Peppa's turn. "Madame Gazelle," she begins, "I don't know what I want to be when I grow up."

"Don't worry, Peppa," says Madame Gazelle. "You have plenty of time to think about it."

"But everybody else knows what they want to be already," Peppa sighs.

Ding! Ding!
The school bell rings and it is time for Peppa and her friends to go home.
"Goodbye, children," says Madame Gazelle.
"Goodbye, Madame Gazelle," say the children all together.

"Hello, my little piggies!" says Mummy Pig. "What did you learn today?"
"Madame Gazelle asked us what we want to be when we grow up," replies Peppa.
"Everybody knows, except me."
"What do you want to be, George?" asks Mummy Pig.
"Dine-saw!" says George. "Grrrrr!"

"Don't worry, Peppa," says Mummy Pig. "You don't have to decide today."
"Do you get to tell people what to do in your computer job?" asks Peppa.
"No," replies Mummy Pig.
"Well, that's no good, then," sighs Peppa.

At bedtime, Peppa asks Daddy Pig what she should do for a job.
"Think of something you like doing," replies Daddy Pig.
"I know!" cries Peppa. "When I grow up I will show everyone
in the world how to jump in muddy puddles!"
"What a good idea!" says Daddy Pig. "Night-night, Peppa. Night-night, George."

Dressing Up!

Can you remember what happened in the story?
What do Peppa and her friends want to be when they grow up?
Draw lines to match everyone to the right costumes.

Grown-Up Jobs

What do you want to be when you grow up?
You can be anything you like! How about an astronaut?
An explorer? Or a scientist? Draw yourself all dressed up
with Peppa and George, then use your colouring pens
or pencils to finish the picture.

Time for Work!

Where does everybody work?
Look at all the uniforms and then draw a line to match
each person to the place where they could work.

Answers: Mr Rhino: road, Dr Elephant: dentist, Zoe Zebra: post van, Peppa: hospital.

Peppa's Circus

Introducing . . . Peppa's Circus!
Look closely at the two pictures of Peppa's super show
and spot six differences between them!

Colour in a circus star as you spot each difference.

Peppa's Pottery

Peppa has made lots of different things on the pottery wheel! What do you think each thing is? Draw lines to match the shapes to the objects.

1. 2. 3. 4. 5.

a. b. c. d. e.

Growing Taller

The flowers in Daddy Pig's garden are growing very tall! Look at the flower bed – which flower is the tallest in each row?

1.

2.

3.

4.

Answers: 1: the second flower, 2: the fifth flower, 3: the sixth flower, 4: the third flower.

Answer: There are four little dinosaurs on the way to George's birthday surprise.

Dino Maze

Hooray, it's George's birthday today!
Can you help George's friends race through the
maze to his roar-some birthday surprise at the finish?
How many little dinosaurs can you count on the way?

Use your brightest colouring pens or pencils to colour in George's bouncy surprise!

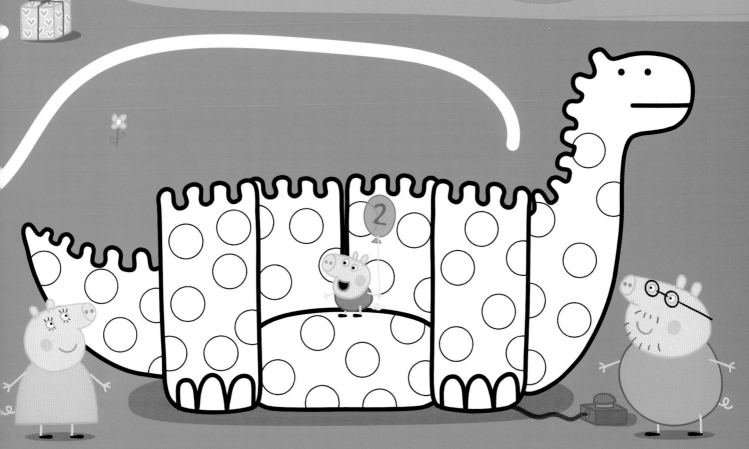

2

Candle Counting

Can you work out how old Peppa and George are by counting the candles on their cakes?

How old are you? Draw the right number of candles on your very own cake and trace the number below.

24   Answers: Peppa is four years old and George is two years old.

Robot Dance

Beep! Beep! Bop! Do the robot! Peppa and her friends are doing a robot dance. Copy their moves so you can do it, too!

Step 1

Step 2

Step 3

Step 4

Step 5

Step 6

Step 7

Step 8
Draw your own robot move here to finish the dance!

25

Story Time
School Project

It's the end of the day at Peppa's playgroup.

"For your school project," says Madame Gazelle, "I want you to go home and make a castle. Use your imagination, and make it as big and fantastic as you like."

"Wow!" gasp the children.

The next morning, Peppa tells Mummy and Daddy Pig that she needs to make a castle.

"Put yoghurt pots on this cereal box, and what have you got?" asks Daddy Pig.

"A box with pots on it," replies Peppa. "No, Daddy. It has to be fantastic and big enough for me to live in."

"I see," replies Daddy Pig.

Over at Suzy Sheep's house, Suzy and Mummy Sheep are looking at the computer.
"Madame Gazelle told you to make a real fairy palace?" asks Mummy Sheep.
"Yes, with all the little fiddly bits," replies Suzy.
"Right," says Mummy Sheep.

Back at Peppa's house, Peppa has drawn a picture.
"This is what my castle looks like, but much, much, much bigger!"
"We'll need to find a very big cardboard box, then," says Mummy Pig.
Just then the doorbell rings. *Ding-dong!*

"Delivery for Daddy Pig," announces Mr Zebra the Postman.
"I don't remember ordering anything this large," says Daddy Pig, opening up the box and pulling out a tiny light bulb. "Why do they use so much packaging?"
"That's good, Daddy," cries Peppa. "We need that box."

After Mr Zebra leaves, Mummy and Daddy Pig start making Peppa's castle.
"It's for you, Peppa," says Mummy Pig when the phone rings. "It's Suzy Sheep."
"How is your project going, Suzy?" asks Peppa.
"I'm doing well . . ." begins Suzy, but then she turns to Mummy Sheep.
"No, Mummy – more pointy and it needs to be taller!"

"How's your project going, Peppa?" asks Suzy.
"It's hard work," replies Peppa, "but my mummy and daddy are helping
a teeny-tiny bit . . ."
"What do you think of this tower, Peppa?" whispers Daddy Pig.
"Very good, but it still looks a bit cardboardy," replies Peppa. Then she says
goodbye to Suzy. "I need to get on with my work now. See you tomorrow."

Mummy and Daddy Pig work very hard to make a fantastic castle.
"What do you think, Peppa?" asks Daddy Pig.
"Wow!" replies Peppa. "It just needs one more thing . . . glitter! Lots and lots of glitter."

The next morning, Peppa and her friends bring in all of their castle creations to playgroup.
"Wow!" gasps Madame Gazelle, seeing Suzy's castle. "That must've been tricky for you to make, Suzy."
"Yes, it was, actually," says Mummy Sheep.

"I made a castle boat!" says Danny Dog.
"Amazing!" gasps Madame Gazelle. "It looks like a lot of work went into it."
"Yes," replies Danny. "My daddy's exhausted!"

"My castle is made out of a cardboard box and lots and lots of glitter," says Peppa.
"And it's big enough for me to live in!"
"It is a very fine, glittery castle," says Madame Gazelle.
"Thank you, Madame Gazelle," replies Mummy Pig.

Madame Gazelle admires all the children's school projects.
"Isn't it wonderful what the children can make, using just their imaginations?" she says.
"Yes, Madame Gazelle," groan the parents.
Everyone loves school projects. Especially the mummies and daddies!

My Dream Castle

Connect the dots to finish the picture.
Then, use your colouring pens or pencils to make it into your very own dream castle. What colour will it be? Does it have flags? Who lives there with you? Use your imagination to make your castle look fantastic!

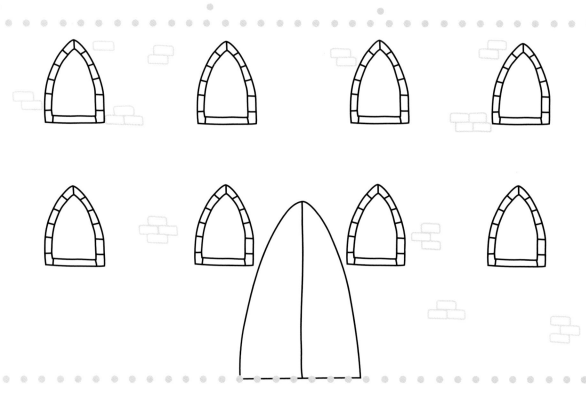

The Prince and Princess Party

Hooray! Peppa, George and their friends are having a party inside your castle! Look at them dancing, then answer the questions.

How many feathers are on George's helmet?

How many blue balloons are there?

What shape is Zoe Zebra's hat?

What colour is Peppa's crown?

Castle Collage

Ask a grown-up to cut out
the opposite page, then cut or tear out the different coloured
shapes. Glue them to the picture to make your own castle collage!

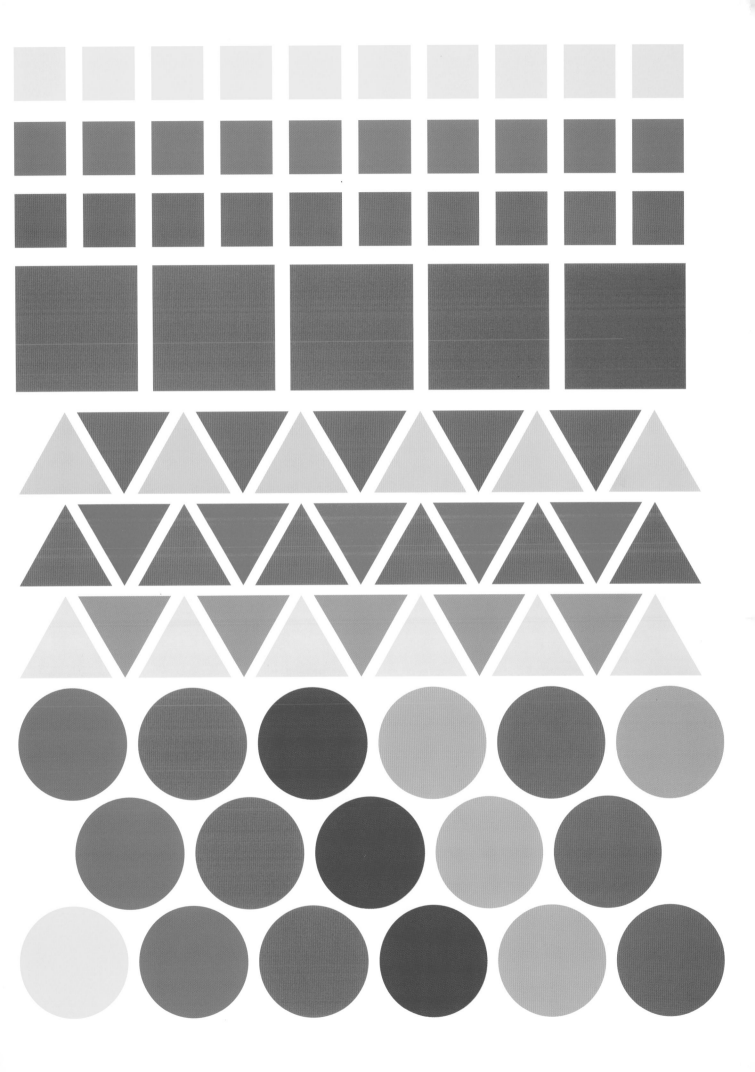

Tin-Can Talk

Peppa and Danny Dog are using tin-can phones to speak to each other. Which string is the one connecting the two cans together? Follow the lines to find out.

A

B

C

Answer: String C connects the two cans together.

Look at all this delicious food! Play the game to collect as many tasty treats as you can for Peppa and George.

Peppa's Yummy

Peppa's Yummy Food

You will need:
- Two small objects to use as counters
- Colouring pens or pencils
- A dice
- Someone to play with

Scrummy Game!

George's Yummy Food

What to do:

1. Each player chooses a blank food card to colour in. One player is "Peppa" and the other player is "George".

2. The younger player goes first. Take it in turns to roll the dice and move around the board.

3. When you land on a piece of food, find the matching picture on your food card and colour it in.

4. Keep moving around the board until one person has coloured in all of their food. That person is the winner!

START HERE

39

Summer-Holiday Adventures

Peppa and her family are going on holiday! Follow the trail from place to place to discover what they get up to.

Packing Bags

Peppa and George are packing their bags for their holiday! Draw circles around what you think they should take.

Flying High

The aeroplane is zooming across the sky to take Peppa and George on holiday! What can they see out of the window? Draw it.

1.

2.

3.

4.

5.

6.

7.

8.

9.

10.

11.

12.

Matching Shells

Peppa has found some pretty shells on the beach. Use your finger or a pencil to draw lines and help Peppa sort the shells into matching pairs.

Splash! Splish! Fish!

Pretend to swim in the sea with Peppa. How many fish can you count?

Answers: The matching pairs are: 1 & 9, 2 & 6, 3 & 5, 4 & 12, 7 & 11, 8 & 10. There are twelve fish.

41

Souvenir Shop

Peppa wants to buy some presents to take home to her family and friends from her holiday. Help her decide what to buy for each person.

Draw a gift from the shop in the box next to each person.

Muddy-Puddle Mess

When they get home from their holiday,
Peppa and her family go in the garden and do their
favourite thing — jumping in muddy puddles! Follow the numbers
to colour in the picture using your colouring pens or pencils.
Make it as muddy as you can!

Snort! Snort!

Splish! Splash!

Key 1 2 3 4
5 6 7 8

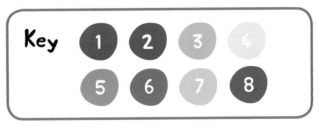

New Shoes

Peppa needs some new shoes! Look at the ones she is dreaming about and find them in the shop. Then, look at the panel and find a pair of shoes for each of Peppa's friends, too.

Which pair of shoes would you choose? If you can't find them in the picture, draw them here.

Tick the white boxes as you find each pair.

Story Time
Masks!

One morning, at Peppa's playgroup, a mysterious masked teacher says, "Hello, children."
"Where is Madame Gazelle?" asks Danny Dog.
"Here I am!" says Madame Gazelle, lifting up her mask.
"Ohhh!" gasp the children in surprise.

"You were in disguise!" says Peppa.
"Yes, I was wearing a mask," says Madame Gazelle. "And today you
will *all* be wearing masks."
"Hooray!" cheer the children.

"First, you must choose a card mask and then you can decorate it," explains Madame Gazelle. "There are lots of paints, pieces of paper, crayons, pom-poms and pipe cleaners on your tables."

"I'm making a butterfly mask," says Peppa, picking up the coloured tissue paper.

Danny Dog is busy using buttons and drinking straws to make antennae for his square mask.

"I'm making a robot mask! Woof!" he tells Madame Gazelle.

"That's brilliant, Danny," says Madame Gazelle.

Suzy Sheep tapes coloured feathers on to her mask.
"I'm making a magic owl mask! Baaa!" she cries.
Pedro makes a superhero mask, while Richard and Rebecca Rabbit both make
carrot masks! "Hee! Hee! We love carrots!" giggles Rebecca.

George has made a dinosaur mask. "Dine-saw! Grrr!" he roars.
"Mine is the solar system with all the planets," says Edmond Elephant. "I have
included Pluto, even though it is only classed as a planetoid."
"Very good," says Madame Gazelle. "So, is everyone finished now?"

All the children tell Madame Gazelle that their masks would look
so much better with glitter on them.
"Glitter, please! Glitter, please! Glitter, please!" they chant.
"OK," says Madame Gazelle, unlocking the glitter cabinet. "But you must
promise to be very careful with it – it gets everywhere!"

At the end of playgroup, the children's parents come to pick them up.
Daddy Pig is the first to arrive. As the door opens he is covered in a cloud of glitter.
"Argh!" he gasps.
"Please remain calm," says Madame Gazelle. "There was a glitter leak, but we now
have it all under control."

"Yes, terrible stuff, glitter," says Daddy Pig, as Madame Gazelle hoovers all the glitter off him.
"Today the children have been making masks," explains Madame Gazelle.

The parents step inside to find the whole classroom covered in glitter.
"Flutter, flutter, flutter," says Peppa, seeing Daddy Pig.
"Excuse me, Mrs Butterfly," says Daddy Pig.
"I'm looking for two little piggies named Peppa and George."
"Ha! Ha! Daddy! We tricked you," says Peppa, taking off her mask. "It's us!"

"Come on, Pedro," says Mummy Pony. "Time to go home."

"I am not Pedro, I'm Super Pony!" shouts Pedro.

"Does Super Pony want to come home or stay here for the night?" asks Mummy Pony.

"Come home with you, please, Mummy," says Pedro.

Madame Gazelle puts her mask on again.

"Haven't we all had fun making wonderful masks?" she asks.

"Who are you?" ask the mummies and daddies.

"It is I . . ." replies Madame Gazelle, taking off her mask. "Madame Gazelle!"

"Hee! Hee!" everyone laughs.

Madame Gazelle loves masks. *Everyone* loves masks!

Making Masks

You can make masks just like
Peppa, George and their friends!

You will need:

Card

Glue

Scissors

Colouring pens
and pencils

Tissue paper, sequins,
pom-poms, glitter, feathers
or other things to decorate
your mask with

Knitting needle or pencil
to make holes in the card

Ribbon or string

What to do

1. Ask a grown-up to glue the masks on to thin card and then cut them out. Don't forget to cut out the holes for the eyes!

2. Colour in your masks and decorate them with tissue paper, sequins, pom-poms, glitter, feathers or anything you like.

3. Ask a grown-up to use a knitting needle or pencil to poke out the holes on the sides. Then thread ribbon or string through the holes so you can tie the mask around your head and keep it on.

Stick in a photo or draw a picture of yourself in your mask here:

Mask Mistakes

Oh no! Some of these masks don't match!
Can you find the odd mask out in each row?
Draw circles around your answers.

57

Guess Who?

Peppa

George

Zoe

Suzy

Aa Bb Cc Dd Ee Ff Gg Hh Ii Jj Kk Ll Mm

Can you recognize everyone at playgroup, even when they have their masks on? Say their names, then draw over the dotted letters to find out if you're right.

Candy

Danny

Pedro

Rebecca

Nn Oo Pp Qq Rr Ss Tt Uu Vv Ww Xx Yy Zz

Going Home

It's time for everyone to go home. Connect the dots to finish the window shapes, then wave goodbye!

1
Who is looking through the round window?

2
Who is peering out of the square window?

3
Who is waving from the rectangular window?

4
Who is peeking through the triangular window?

Answers: 1. Daddy Pig, 2. Peppa, 3. George, 4. Mummy Pig.

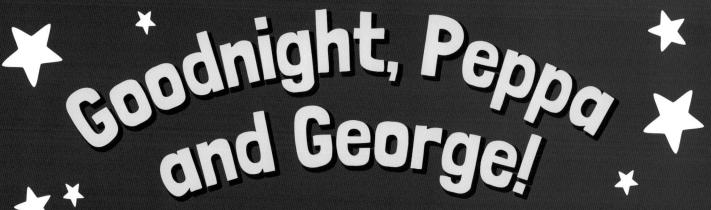

Goodnight, Peppa and George!

Peppa and George are going to bed.
Read the rhyme, and sing the words when you see the pictures.
You'll soon send Peppa and George drifting off to sleep.
Zzzzzz! Snort! Snort!

Twinkle, twinkle, little ,

How I wonder what you are.

Up above the 🌍 so high,

Like a ◇ in the ⬚.

Twinkle, twinkle, little ⭐,

How I wonder what you are.

Key

⭐ star   ◇ diamond

🌍 world   ⬚ sky

Look out for these other great Peppa Pig books!

CD and audio download